THE TOP TEN FILM THEMES TO PLAY ON PIANO

WISE PUBLICATIONS
part of The Music Sales Group
London / New York / Paris / Sydney / Copenhagen / Berlin / Madrid / Hong Kong / Tokyo

Published by
Wise Publications
14-15 Berners Street,
London W1T 3LJ, UK.

Exclusive Distributors:
Music Sales Limited
Distribution Centre, Newmarket Road,
Bury St Edmunds, Suffolk IP33 3YB, UK.
Music Sales Corporation
180 Madison Avenue, 24th Floor,
New York NY 10016, USA.
Music Sales Pty Limited
Level 4, Lisgar House,
30-32 Carrington Street,
Sydney, NSW 2000 Australia.

Order No. AM1012264
ISBN 978-1-78558-401-5

Notes written by Sandy Burnett.

Photographs courtesy of:
Page 5 – 20th Century-Fox/Getty Images
Page 10 – Buyenlarge/Getty Images
Page 16 – Universal/Getty Images
Page 24 – United Artist/Getty Images
Page 28 – Universal/Getty Images
Page 34 – Thomas Samson/AFP/Getty Images
Page 38 – AF archive/Alamy Stock Photo
Page 44 – United Artists/Getty Images
Page 50 – Moviestore collection Ltd/Alamy Stock Photo
Page 56 – AF archive/Alamy Stock Photo

Printed in the EU.

THE TOP TEN FILM THEMES TO PLAY ON PIANO

Putting together our selection of much-loved film themes to play on piano has been a particular pleasure for us, but be warned: we'll be plonking you down in a variety of exhilarating eras and locations. In no particular order, they include a gladiatorial arena in Ancient Rome, Juliet's balcony as she calls out for Romeo, bombed-out Warsaw in the dark days of the Second World War, the gritty world of Scandi-noir, and a secluded Pacific island where a team of scientists just happen to be breeding dinosaurs… So make sure your vaccinations are up to date, and enjoy the ride!

BALCONY SCENE
FROM *ROMEO + JULIET*

COMPOSERS: Craig Armstrong/Marius de Vries/
Nellee Hooper/Tim Atack/Desirée Weekes

COMPOSED: 1996

'O Romeo, Romeo! wherefore art thou Romeo?' Juliet's balcony cry, and the Shakespeare play it comes from, has lent itself for reinvention by all sorts of artists from many succeeding ages. Think of the sweeping symphonic sound of Tchaikovsky's tone poem, for example, and Leonard Bernstein's gangland reworking of the play in *West Side Story*. Director Baz Luhrmann took his turn in 1996 with an updated film adaptation – note the '+' instead of 'and' in the title – appointing Craig Armstrong to compose the score. Successfully, as it turned out: the two collaborated once again on *Moulin Rouge!* five years later, a movie that similarly updated turn-of-the-century Parisian cabaret to a more modern era.

What Armstrong likes about working with Luhrmann is that he is given a lot of freedom to try out musical ideas in any way he wants, to find his own creative direction. In the case of *Romeo + Juliet*, working in collaboration with Nellee Hooper and Marius de Vries, Armstrong opens his 'Balcony Scene' theme with a rhapsodic opening statement for solo piano, before a string orchestra takes over with a series of soft held chords – this is the *legato* section on the second page of our arrangement here.

BALCONY SCENE

FROM *ROMEO + JULIET*

Craig Armstrong/Marius de Vries/Nellee Hooper/Tim Atack/Desirée Weekes

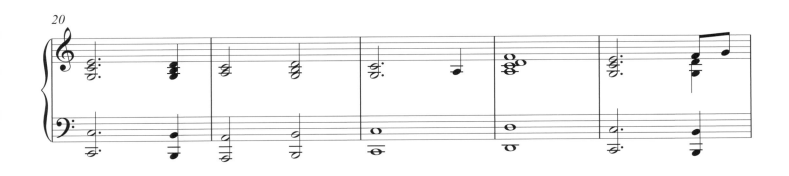

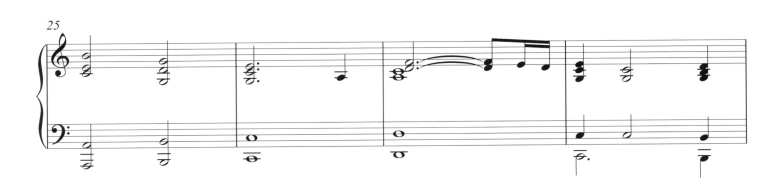

THE HEART ASKS PLEASURE FIRST

FROM *THE PIANO*

COMPOSER: Michael Nyman
COMPOSED: 1993

Sometimes the most serene music starts out in the most unlikely of circumstances, and that's the case with 'The Heart Asks Pleasure First'. It was one of a series of pieces that film composer Michael Nyman wrote in the early 1990s for director Jane Campion, who had engaged him to work on her film *The Piano*. He told *The Guardian* newspaper that he wrote it 'in a house full of builders in France, on a synthesiser resting on a Black & Decker workbench, because there was no piano or table. A most unromantic setting for such a romantic piece.' Be that as it may, 'The Heart Asks Pleasure First' went on to make a perfect main theme for the movie; a busy left-hand accompaniment supports a right-hand melody that's tinged by the colour of Scottish folk music.

The film's heroine, Ada, was a mute Scottish woman who had been sold in an arranged marriage to a frontiersman in New Zealand in the mid-nineteenth century. Unable to speak, Ada had one sure-fire way of communicating: her real voice came through in her piano playing.

THE HEART ASKS PLEASURE FIRST

FROM *THE PIANO*

Michael Nyman

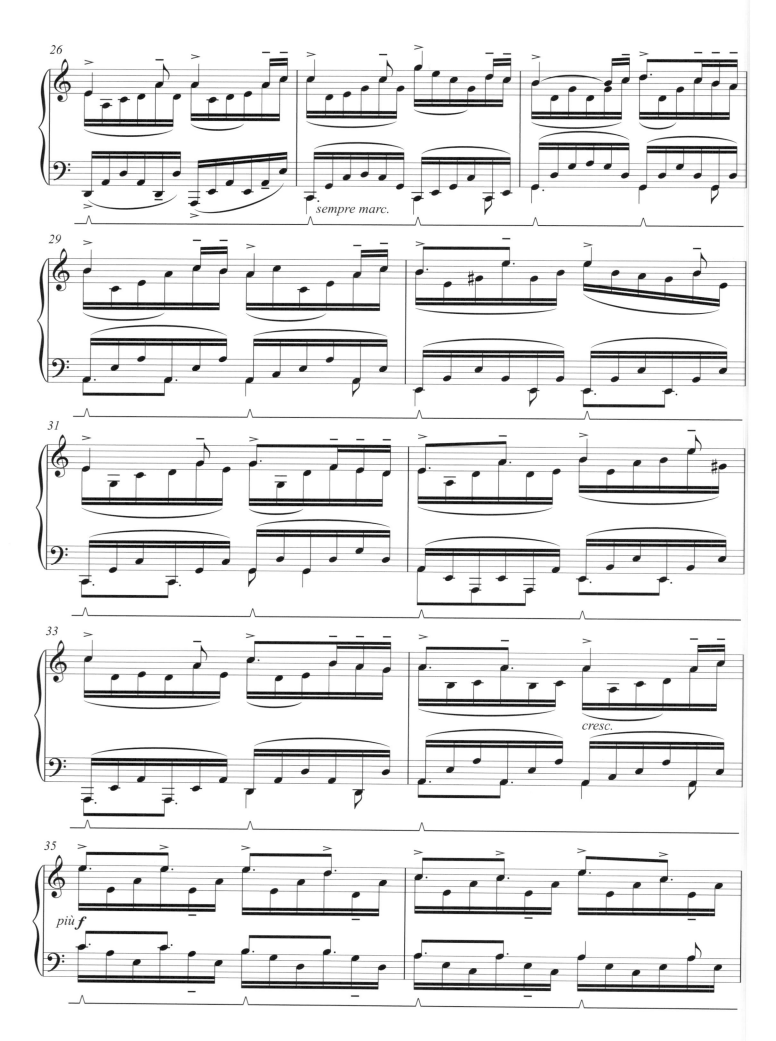

HONOR HIM/NOW WE ARE FREE
FROM GLADIATOR

COMPOSERS: Hans Zimmer/Lisa Gerrard/Klaus Badelt
COMPOSED: 2000

Director Ridley Scott and movie company Dreamworks saw in the millennium with one of the most successful historical epic films to be made in recent years. Playing fast and loose with the facts of Ancient Roman history, it describes how a fictional general Maximus Decimus Meridius (Russell Crowe) is betrayed and reduced to slavery by Commodus, the real-life son of Emperor Marcus Aurelius. Maximus gets his own back in dramatic fashion — and where better to do so than in the spectacular setting of the Colosseum in Rome, in front of hundreds of bloodthirsty spectators?

Although Gladiator cost a cool hundred million dollars to make, it had recouped all of its production budget a fortnight after it opened in May 2000. It went on to take almost half a million dollars at the box office worldwide, as well as picking up five Academy Awards and many other honours along the way. This selection from Gladiator's soundtrack brings two of its standout themes together. 'Honor Him', in gentle triple time, leads into the driving lyricism of 'Now We Are Free', a number that Lisa Gerrard sings during the film's closing sequence.

HONOR HIM/NOW WE ARE FREE

FROM *GLADIATOR*

Hans Zimmer/Lisa Gerrard/Klaus Badelt

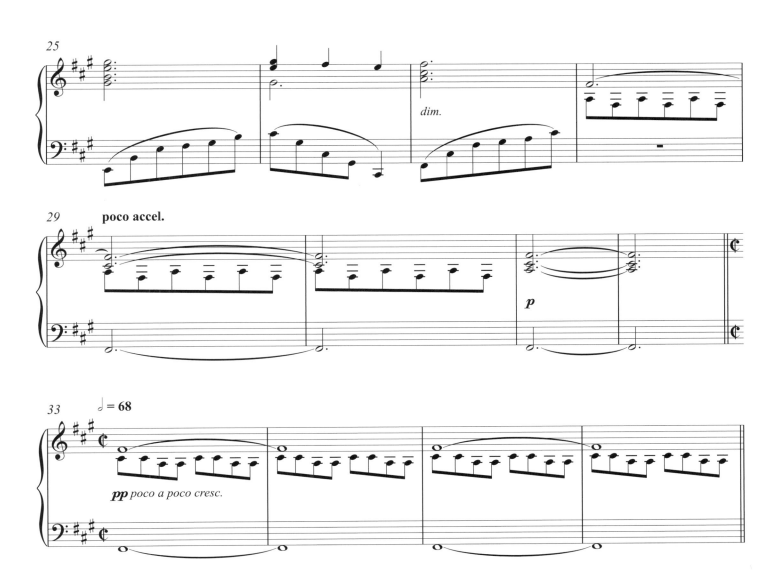

II. NOW WE ARE FREE

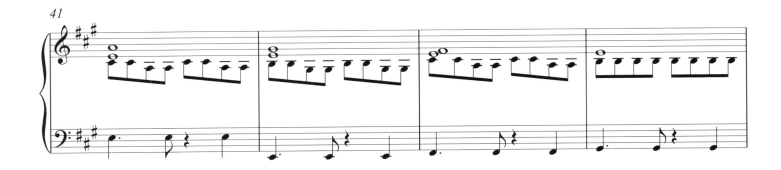

THE JAMES BOND THEME

COMPOSER: Monty Norman
COMPOSED: 1962

When the first James Bond movie came out in 1962, the tuxedo-clad spy hero announced himself to the world's movie goers with the sound of one of the most unforgettable film themes of all. We have Monty Norman to thank for that; at the time he was approached to write for the film, he was working as a singer and composer in the world of West End musicals. In scouting around for a theme to encapsulate Bond, Norman suddenly remembered a song he'd written a few years before for a musical set in Trinidad. He took out the words, firmed up the rhythm, and asked a young arranger by the name of John Barry to score it for big band.

James Bond had already been around for a decade by that time in literary form, the hero of a series of novels by Ian Fleming. He was a writer who knew Bond's world of espionage first-hand from his time as a British intelligence officer during the Second World War. Casting Sean Connery as Bond's first movie incarnation turned out to be a masterstroke, and Monty Norman's music matched the dapper Scotsman perfectly. Just like Bond himself, the theme is charming, charismatic, and just a little bit menacing.

THE JAMES BOND THEME

Monty Norman

JURASSIC PARK THEME

COMPOSER: John Williams

COMPOSED: 1993

No selection of film themes would be complete without John Williams, who for many movie-goers is an undisputed master of the genre. In a career spanning six decades, he has created soundtracks to some of the most commercially successful films of his time, with a list of credits as long as your arm. In particular, Williams has enjoyed a wonderful collaboration with director Steven Spielberg – a relationship that started out back in 1974. *Jurassic Park* was the twelfth film they worked on together.

The story is set on a fictional island in the Pacific where a billionaire philanthropist and a team of scientists have created a wildlife park of real live dinosaurs, cloning them by taking dinosaur DNA from the bodies of mosquitoes which had been preserved in amber. What could possibly go wrong? Well, quite a lot, as it happens – providing plenty of drama for John Williams to sink his teeth into. He came up with music that captures either the spirit-soaring excitement of the scientists or the feelings of terror that only being attacked by a Tyrannosaurus can create. Hence the aspirational hymn-like tune, which appears marked 'reverently', and the powerful scoring later on in this 'Jurassic Park Theme'. Feel free to make that piano sound as orchestral as you can!

JURASSIC PARK THEME

John Williams

Reflectively

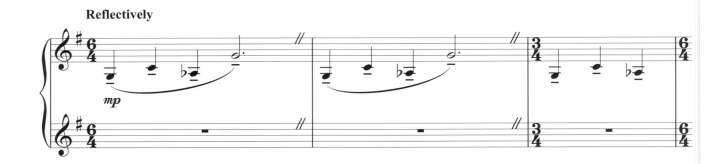

Tenderly

a tempo

Reverently

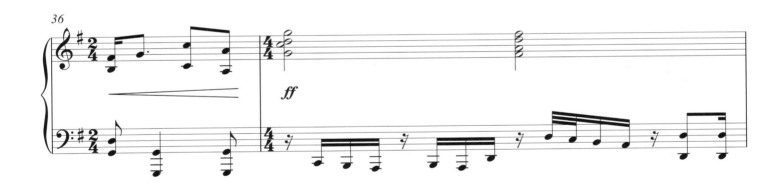

THE KING'S SPEECH

COMPOSER: Alexandre Desplat
COMPOSED: 2010

Prolific Oscar-winning composer Alexandre Desplat has scored the music for a couple of royal movies in recent years: there's this 2010 film about George VI, and the earlier movie *The Queen* from 2006 about George VI's daughter, Her Majesty Queen Elizabeth II. He was assisted by Pete Cobin, chief engineer at London's world famous Abbey Road studios, who unearthed some vintage microphones that the British royal family had used back in those days, which helped create just the right recording quality for the soundtrack. There's dedication to duty…

The challenge for Desplat, and indeed his opportunity, was to come up with music that would take the place of words while telling the story of how the Duke of York, on the point of becoming king in 1936, turned to the unconventional Australian speech therapist Lionel Logue for help in overcoming his speech impediment.

Desplat's music encapsulates both sides of the story: the warmth of the friendship between the two men and the agonising handicap of a stammer which meant that the king's speech – and *The King's Speech* – kept breaking down into silence. This is reflected in the two distinct sections of the main theme; its start is warm and flowing, its end, cold and bleak.

THE KING'S SPEECH

Alexandre Desplat

NOCTURNE IN C♯ MINOR

FROM *THE PIANIST*

COMPOSER: Frédéric Chopin
COMPOSED: 1830

One of the greatest Romantic pianists of all, Frédéric Chopin left his native Poland at the age of 20 and settled in Paris, where his delicate and poetic playing made him a must-have guest at the city's artistic salons. Dying a few months before his fortieth birthday, Chopin left this exquisite nocturne as a dedication to his sister, but it wasn't published for a further 26 years.

Winding the clock forward to the start of the Second World War, as Germany began its invasion of Warsaw in September 1939, the last piece of music to be broadcast on Polish radio before it closed down was this very nocturne. Wladyslaw Szpilman was the performer, a man who then had to hide as bombs destroyed his city and Jewish people like him were being hunted down and sent to the death camps. Szpilman survived partly through the assistance of a German captain who advised him how to escape the onslaught, and for whom Szpilman used to perform this piece in return. It's an extraordinary story that Roman Polanski tells in his 2002 movie *The Pianist*. Sadly, Szpilman didn't live to see it – he had died in Warsaw a couple of years before at the age of 88.

NOCTURNE IN C# MINOR

FROM *THE PIANIST*

Frédéric Chopin

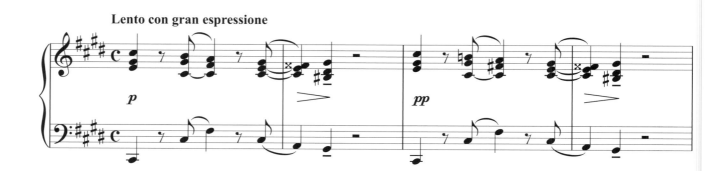

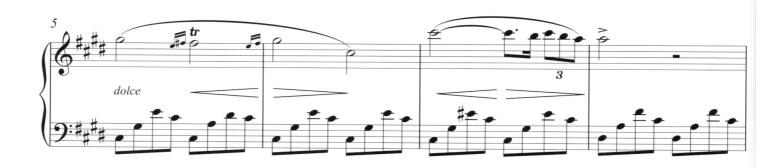

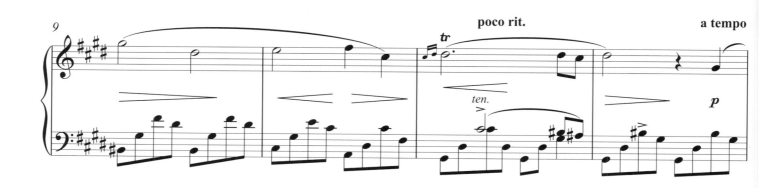

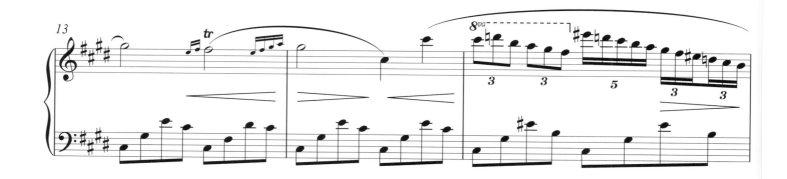

41

THE PINK PANTHER THEME

COMPOSER: Henry Mancini
COMPOSED: 1963

With four Academy Awards, a Golden Globe and twenty Grammy Awards to his name, the late Henry Mancini could justifiably lay claim to being one of the most significant film composers there's ever been. He's also someone we can credit for making the sound of jazz such a core element of film scores throughout the 50s and 60s, a side of his art he had the chance to perfect when he joined the Glenn Miller Orchestra as composer and pianist straight after the Second World War.

'The Pink Panther Theme' is one of his most brilliant moments of inspiration. He was booked by director Blake Edwards to write the music for the film. Although *The Pink Panther* franchise became a vehicle for the comic genius of Peter Sellers, the first film was conceived as a showcase for the dashing David Niven, in the role of a phantom jewel thief. It was for him, a character who in the screenplay often slunk around on tiptoes, that Mancini wrote what went on to become 'The Pink Panther Theme'. In its original scoring, a slightly sleazy sax plays the main theme, underpinned by acoustic double bass and later big band, all getting under way with that unforgettable high 'ting' chord on piano.

THE PINK PANTHER THEME

Henry Mancini

SCHINDLER'S LIST THEME

COMPOSER: John Williams
COMPOSED: 1993

Based on a prize-winning book by Thomas Keneally, *Schindler's List* tells Oskar Schindler's remarkable story. He was a black-market businessman in German-occupied Poland during the Second World War who became an unlikely humanitarian hero. As he realised the horrific fate that awaited the Jewish community in Krakov, Schindler transformed his factory there into a refuge for Jewish people, eventually saving hundreds of lives during the course of the war.

Steven Spielberg shot his 1993 movie adaptation entirely in black and white; it featured Liam Neeson in the role of Schindler,

Ben Kingsley as his Jewish accountant and Ralph Fiennes as the German officer Amon Göth. To write the music, Spielberg engaged the doyen of Hollywood film composers, John Williams. The score he created went on to be festooned with awards, including an Academy Award for Best Original Score, a BAFTA for Best Film Music, and a Grammy for Best Score Soundtrack for Visual Media. Presented here for solo piano, the main theme in its original version was written for violin and orchestra. The soloist on the soundtrack, the eminent virtuoso Itzhak Perlman, has gone on record as saying that his contribution to the film is one of his proudest moments.

SCHINDLER'S LIST THEME

John Williams

WARNING CRY
FROM *THE GIRL WITH THE DRAGON TATTOO*

COMPOSER: Jacob Groth
COMPOSED: 2009

24-year-old Lisbeth Salander might be short of stature, but she has formidable determination, as well as a genius for computer hacking and a taste for piercings and body art. It would definitely not be a good idea to get on the wrong side of her, especially if she has a tattoo gun in her hand…

Lisbeth was the creation of author Stieg Larsson, who wrote a trilogy of Swedish-language novels before he died at the age of 44. His books became best-sellers and spawned two movie adaptations, both of them gripping in their own way. A Hollywood one came out in 2011 starring Daniel Craig and Rooney Mara, but a BAFTA Award-winning Swedish film treatment got there first, directed by Niels Arden Oplev. Creating the soundtrack for that earlier version was Danish composer Jacob Groth, who'd already had a long TV scoring career before *The Girl With The Dragon Tattoo* came along. Though if you sat through the trilogy and didn't notice Jacob Groth's music, that's absolutely fine by him. In his opinion, music for movies is something that should be felt rather than heard.

WARNING CRY

FROM *THE GIRL WITH THE DRAGON TATTOO*

Jacob Groth

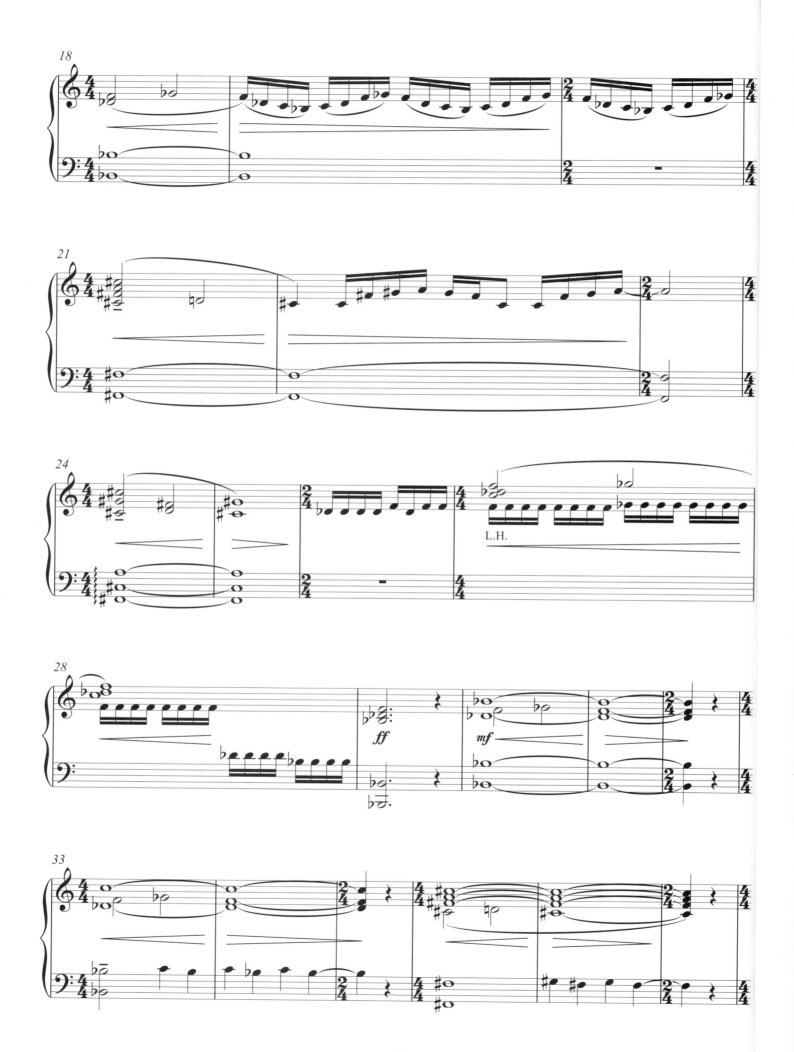

123456789

Recommended for you...

Michael Nyman:
Film Music For
Solo Piano
CH61400

Contemporary Film
Scores For
Solo Piano
AM1012066

Frozen Planet,
The Blue Planet,
Planet Earth:
The Piano Album
CH81653

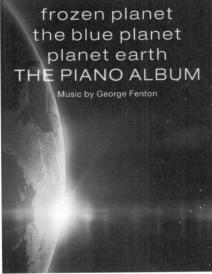

Film Scores For
Solo Piano
AM1010537

Africa: The
Piano Album
CH81664

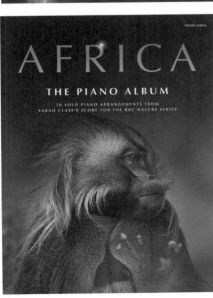

Ludovico Einaudi:
Film Music
CH83677

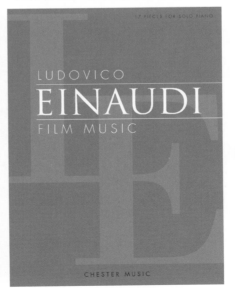

THE TOP TEN...

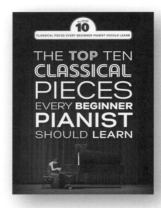

THE TOP TEN
CLASSICAL PIECES
EVERY BEGINNER
PIANIST
SHOULD LEARN
AM1012231

THE TOP TEN
MOST BEAUTIFUL
PIECES TO PLAY
ON PIANO
AM1012253

THE TOP TEN
CHRISTMAS
SONGS TO PLAY
ON PIANO
AM1012484

THE TOP TEN
LOVE SONGS
TO PLAY
ON PIANO
AM1012275

THE TOP TEN
PIANO SONGS
OF ALL TIME
AM1012242

THE TOP TEN
CONTEMPORARY
CLASSICAL PIECES
TO PLAY ON PIANO
AM1012286

THE TOP TEN
MOST CALMING
PIECES TO PLAY
ON PIANO
AM1012319

THE TOP TEN
FILM THEMES TO
PLAY ON PIANO
AM1012264

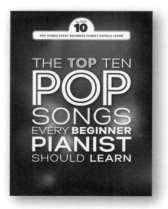

THE TOP TEN
POP SONGS EVERY
BEGINNER PIANIST
SHOULD LEARN
AM1012297

THE TOP TEN
JAZZ SONGS TO
PLAY ON PIANO
AM1012308